BROWN BEARS OF BROOKS RIVER

RONALD SQUIBB AND TAMARA OLSON

PHOTOGRAPHY BY JAMES GAVIN

ILLUSTRATIONS BY CATHERINE SCHNEIDER

© 1993 by R.C. Squibb
Kodiak, AK 99615-3904
All Rights Reserved.

Printed by Lorraine Press, Salt Lake City

Edited by Rose Houk and Shelley Williams

Design by Jeff D. Clawson

ISBN # 0-9638016-0-0

Young bear eating salmon.

Foreword

We wrote this book to help the public better understand brown bears and to enrich the experience of visitors to Brooks River. Our observations, conclusions, and opinions are the result of some 2,600 hours of observations of bears, and hundreds more hours of personal experience with bears, at Brooks River and vicinity between 1988 and 1992. We also included information from other sources to provide a more complete understanding of those bears. Our statements and conclusions do not necessarily represent the positions or policy of the National Park Service.

Many of our conclusions depended on identifying unmarked bears between seasons and from year to year. We identified bears by a combination of scars, facial features, shape, behavior, and colors and patterns of their coats. Their coats were least reliable because they changed as the bears shed their old winter coats and grew new ones. We were able to identify most of the adult bears that regularly used Brooks River. Subadults were much more difficult to recognize because they usually had no major scars and rapidly changed in appearance as they grew; we were able to identify only a few of these bears from year to year.

During the study, we gave each bear a number in order to identify it in our records; we gave most a name as well. We used those names when recording observations because they were easier to remember; we use them in this book for the same reason. The bears are not aware of our names for them and their lives are not affected by them. Be careful that your perception of the bears remains equally unaffected. None of the bears at Brooks River are tame; all are wild and free ranging, even those that have learned to tolerate people. You should behave with caution and respect around all bears.

The Authors

Bear walks Naknek beach at dusk.

The Cycle of Brooks River

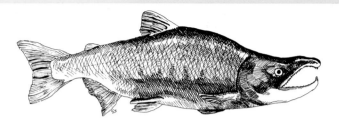

Brooks River lies within Katmai National Park at the base of the Alaska Peninsula. The river flows for only a mile and a half, draining Brooks Lake into Naknek Lake, the largest lake within the park. Brown bears (the coastal form of the grizzly bear, *Ursus arctos*) pass through this area only occasionally during spring as it offers them no more opportunity for food than the surrounding country. Only when the migrating sockeye salmon (*Oncorhynchus nerka*) arrive, do large numbers of bears concentrate at Brooks River.

Each year from late June until the end of July, salmon numbering in the hundreds of thousands run into Brooks River. Most of these salmon migrate through the river, bound for the long tributary creeks of Brooks Lake; tens of thousands remain to spawn in Brooks River itself. Midway up the river the salmon meet a six-foot-high waterfall, Brooks Falls. As they mass in the pools beneath it and jump the falls, the salmon are vulnerable to bears. The white water scarcely conceals the fins and backs of the densely packed salmon when large schools crowd beneath the falls.

A few bears anticipate the run and arrive before the salmon. Bears continue to arrive at Brooks River through July, their numbers peaking in the middle of the month. About twenty-five bears, excluding dependent young, fish Brooks River for several days or weeks during July; several others pass through for only a day or two. Although fishing is the main occupation of bears at Brooks River, there are usually several adults still courting and mating during early July.

The bears concentrate at Brooks Falls where they compete for a chance at a fish. A few bears wait atop the lip of the falls to grab jumping salmon from the air as they clear the top. Several wait in the pools below the falls to grab salmon from the white water or to pin them against the bottom. Still others wait on the periphery for fishing spots to open when more dominant bears leave. Those who cannot hold a place to fish at Brooks Falls search the lower river for salmon carcasses and scraps that wash downriver.

Bears begin to leave Brooks River in search of better fishing by the last week of July, even though salmon may still be jumping the falls. Some bears move with the salmon into the shallow tributaries of Brooks Lake, others go to tributaries of Naknek Lake, and a few prob-

Chance and Survival

Goatee was already an old bear by 1989. She occasionally fished Brooks Falls that July with her cubs in their first summer. While she fished, she would send the two spring cubs up a tall spruce tree just downriver of the Brooks Falls Bear-Viewing Platform. On the morning of July 21, she returned to fish the white water beneath the far side of the falls after sharing a fish with her cubs. Instead of climbing back up the spruce tree after their meal, the cubs remained on the bank watching their mother fish.

A young adult male came out of the alders upriver and rushed the cubs. Both cubs ran, separating. The male caught one cub in the tall grass by the viewing platform and carried its body into the woods. The other cub escaped to the safety of the spruce tree.

Goatee continued fishing under the noisy falls, unaware of the attack. When she returned half an hour later, she found the distraught cub bawling in the tree but only the blood of its sibling. Goatee followed the trails of her fleeing cubs and their pursuer again and again, pausing only to smell the bloody grass.

The surviving cub eventually climbed down the tree to her mother. But the cub hesitated to leave the safety of the spruce tree and ran back to it repeatedly, climbing and then descending it, before venturing out a little farther on each successive foray with her

Goatee as a single bear in July 1988.

mother. Whenever Goatee moved too far from the tree, the cub bawled. After more than an hour with her cub, Goatee returned to fishing and caught two salmon. She shared the second with her cub.

Goatee behaved much more aggressively toward other bears that afternoon than was her nature. She growled at the innocent male Bullet as he walked nearby, and she chased the small female Petite forty yards along the river bank.

Goatee remained obviously distressed for the next couple of days. Nevertheless, she had to continue to fish and provide for her surviving spring cub, Chowmane.

Diver catches spawned salmon, autumn 1992.

ably travel farther. In those shallow streams, the bears can efficiently attack spawning salmon. Brooks River receives little use by bears during August of most years because its deep water protects the vigorous salmon there.

Bears return to Brooks River as spawned salmon deplete their energy reserves and begin to die. The weakened fish become vulnerable even in deep water, and their carcasses are carried downriver to collect along the banks and in slow water. Bears will search the lower river and shallow waters of Naknek Lake both day and night for these spent salmon.

A few bears are again fishing Brooks River by the end of August, and bear numbers increase into October. About thirty bears, excluding young, fish the river for several days or weeks during the autumn; several others pass through. Many are the same bears that used the river during July, while others are there only during autumn. Brooks River is unique in the region because it provides salmon to bears as early as July and as late as the end of October.

September and October are important months for bears. They increase their intake, eating vast quantities of food in order to put on fat for denning. Spawned salmon are available as are ripening berries, and the bears readily avail themselves of both. By November, or weeks earlier in cold years,

The young male Speck finds a salmon carcass in autumn 1988.

bears begin departing Brooks River for their dens. Pregnant females typically den first, followed by females with young, other bears, and finally the older males. Many of the bears that fish Brooks River den on surrounding mountains such as Kelez, Katolinat, Dumpling, and La Gorce; others may den much farther away.

Bears leave Brooks River in August to fish shallow streams where sockeye salmon are more vulnerable.

Bright sockeye salmon must surmount Brooks Falls to continue their upriver migration.

Large male fishes Brooks Falls, July 1992.

*Confrontation over a fishing spot at Brooks Falls,
July 1992.*

Peaceful Coexistence

Bears come to Brooks River to use a critical resource in their annual struggle to survive and reproduce. People visit the river to enjoy a vacation from their own competitive world. Both bears and humans are accustomed to being the dominant animal in their environment. The peaceful coexistence of these two species at such high densities is amazing given the often desperate nature of the competition among the bears.

During the years of our study, there was an average of about 100 visitors on Brooks River each day for the nearly 100-day visitor season. On peak days in July, more than 200 people were sometimes in the area.

People cannot be ignored as a major part of the environment at Brooks River, indeed at any Alaskan salmon stream where airplanes bring people for sport fishing or bear viewing. Human use affects bears at two different levels. First, bears that cannot tolerant people may leave or avoid an area when people are present. When an important area is continuously occupied by people, then the bear population must adjust to a reduced food base. Second, some bears learn to modify their behavior around people.

Learning to Accept People

The most common way that bears learn from people involves a process called habituation. Habituation simply means getting accustomed to something. Bears, especially adults, are cautious and conservative animals. A bear that has never seen people will likely avoid them on its first encounter; but, if nothing bad happens to the bear, it may learn after several encounters that there is no need to run away.

Habituation among Brooks River bears varies from bears that flee at the scent of a person, to those that fish apparently undisturbed even with people lining both banks of the river. We called bears habituated if they consistently tolerated people at fifty yards; those that consistently withdrew at distances of fifty yards or more were defined as nonhabituated.

Bears that habituate to people gain an advantage–access to more resources than if they remained intolerant. Because larger bears get first choice of fishing spots, the more subordinate and vulnerable bears may have no choice but to fish where people are, hence they are pressured to habituate.

Subadults and females with cubs need salmon, and the only places on Brooks River where they can fish without encountering large bears are often in the lower river near Brooks Lodge and in the cutbank when people are present. After only a couple of weeks of interacting with people on Brooks River, subadults become comfortable, sometimes even bold, around people. Similarly, habituated females sometimes bring their cubs to the mouth of the river, and the cubs learn to tolerate people from watching how their mothers behave.

Several subadults that appeared habituated to people continued to behave so as adults. We did observe a few bold subadults begin to avoid people as they grew older. However, once a bear established its behavior around people as an adult, it was unlikely to change much. Individual bears did, of course, vary their behavior with circumstance and need.

In the autumn of 1990, the adult male Speck would not fish the lower river alone when people were fishing or standing along the banks. However, he would fish near people in the company of his habituated playmate Bullet. Since that autumn, Speck has returned to his old habits of leaving the river when people arrive.

Females often change their patterns when they have cubs. The nonhabituated females Flame and Lucy always avoided people when they were single, yet with yearling cubs they were sometimes in areas near people. The habituated females Petite and Goatee made similar changes in their use of the river. When they had cubs, they spent much of their time near people in the lower river and around Brooks Lodge. When these same females were single, they rarely came downriver during July, using Brooks Falls almost exclusively; and in autumn, they were seldom near the lodge or in the mouth of the river. Old Mom was the only habituated female to frequent areas near people when she was single. These patterns indicate again that mothers probably change their behavior in order to feed and protect their young.

From 1988 to 1992, five to seven habituated adults used Brooks River during any season. These were the adult bears most commonly seen by visitors in places other than the falls. They included most prominently Diver, and the reproducing females Goatee, Petite, Old Mom, Fluff, and Daisy, as well as Bullet, Bear #77, and Ester. During those same years, as many as fourteen nonhabituated adults used the river regularly during July, and as many as seventeen during autumn. Prominent nonhabituated adults included the large males Gramps and Conan, the reproducing females Beauty, Flame, and Lucy, as well as the adult males Panda, Cinnamon, and Speck.

Although a bear has become habituated to people, that behavior does not mean that it "likes" people. Tolerance, or perhaps acceptance, better describes its behavior. Habituated bears go near people in order to fish certain areas, not because they are attracted to the people there.

This fact was apparent in the changes in behavior of several bears. Bullet's use of the lower river during July decreased as he became an adult, probably because he had grown large enough to displace most other bears from his preferred fishing spot at the lip of Brooks Falls. Most habituated females used the lower river extensively during July only when they had cubs. Without a reason to avoid concentrations of bears, these females used the falls more when they were single. The large male Diver did not use the mouth of the river often during July unless he could catch fish there as fast as he could at the falls, as happened during 1990.

The Dilemma of Shy Bears

In late June and early July 1990, sockeye salmon swarmed into Brooks River in numbers rarely seen. The crowding was so great as the large schools crammed themselves against Brooks Falls that an exceptional number of salmon died and washed back downriver. Hundreds of bright silver carcasses littered the bottom of the oxbow and mouth, and bears were picking them up as fast as they normally would in autumn. While bears in the mouth of the river took only ten minutes to find a carcass, those that remained at the falls spent fourteen minutes for each catch.

Yet not all bears came to fish at this temporary hot spot near Brooks Lodge. Only subadults and the few habituated adults used the area. The larger number of nonhabituated adults did not fish the mouth of the river, probably because of the anglers in the river and the human traffic near the lodge. By having learned to tolerate people, the habituated adults had gained an advantage over those adults whose intolerance of people kept them away from the best fishing.

Brooks Falls during July appears to be an exception to the pattern of nonhabituated adults avoiding people. During most daylight hours in July, the Brooks Falls viewing platform is at or near capacity—thirty or more people crowd onto the platform to watch several bears fish from twenty-five to seventy yards away. The majority of adult bears fishing there will not tolerate people at such close distances in other parts of the river. An understanding of this situation clarifies how these shy adults balance their need for salmon and their intolerance of people.

Predictable human behavior seems very important to nonhabituated adults. At Brooks Falls, people stay off the river and remain on

Old Mom's cubs stay dry by crossing on the bridge while their mother fishes in the river, September 1992.

Behaviorally Constrained

Early one morning in July 1990, only four of us stood on the platform watching the large male Gramps fish the plunge pool. Gramps preferred that spot. He sometimes fished there little more than twenty-five yards from a platform full of people, much closer than the seventy to one hundred yards that he stayed from people when he fished the oxbow during September.

From across the river, a large blond male bear entered Brooks Falls. The male was tense; the saliva hanging from his half-opened mouth showed his stress. He approached Gramps. Gramps chose not to confront the younger, and probably stronger, bear. He withdrew from the plunge pool, his ears down, and backed to a place directly underneath the front of the viewing platform. Gramps sat there and faced his challenger. Standing over Gramps, we watched the younger male. He had advanced halfway across the river, where he faced Gramps, but he would come no closer. He became obviously more stressed, seemingly unable to take the plunge pool or displace his rival while we were on the platform. Finally, the younger male withdrew into the woods across from us. Gramps resumed fishing the plunge pool.

Gramps in July 1992 with a distinct scar on his muzzle.

the viewing platform to the south of the falls. Access is mostly by one trail, and people are rarely there at dusk and dawn. These simple and predictable human patterns seem acceptable to bears that avoid other parts of the river where human use is unrestricted.

It is not that the shy adults become habituated to people at Brooks Falls. The bears that are least tolerant of people still tend to stay away from people on the viewing platform by using the north side of the falls. More tolerant bears use the south side, which incidently has the better fishing. The nonhabituated adults strike a balance between the attraction of fishing at the falls and the repulsion of the people there. Just as a hungry mother may risk bringing her cubs near other bears at the falls, a nonhabituated adult may risk coming near people at the falls for a chance to catch a fish. Brooks Falls is a powerful attraction for bears during July. Nevertheless, several of the nonhabituated adults still cannot tolerate a full viewing platform, and will fish only during the odd hours when few people are there.

Choosing Where to Fish

A bear's decision of where to fish seems to be based on the locations of three things: good fishing, larger bears, and people.

Habituated adults are the least constrained. They will use whatever part of the river provides the most salmon. However, habituated females with young also respond to the presence of large bears, and with spring cubs sometimes avoid people, as well. These families are less likely to use Brooks Falls in July, and they avoid large males in the autumn.

Subadult bear searches the oxbow for salmon carcasses after Brooks Lodge has closed, 1992.

Bear fishes for spawned salmon in cutbank, autumn 1988.

Subadults cannot compete with older bears, and are threatened by them. They tend to fish where there are the fewest older bears, which is often near people. Subadults fish the lower river in both seasons, and typically use Brooks Falls when most older bears are absent. Many subadults rest in the forest north and west of Brooks Lodge and the campground. That concentration of people seems to prevent most adult bears from moving into those areas.

Nonhabituated adults prefer to avoid people; they rarely use the river mouth, even in autumn. Nonhabituated females with young are most constrained because they try to avoid both people and larger bears. These families often are left with few choices for fishing on Brooks River when people are present.

The attraction of good fishing must be very strong to bring nonhabituated adults near people. Even then, these intolerant bears require a situation where human behavior is predictable, as at Brooks Falls. In autumn, few nonhabituated bears use Brooks River before the lodge closes in the middle of September.

It became clear in September 1992 when Brooks Lodge extended its season by a week, that these bears were waiting for the end of the visitor season before they would use the river. These less tolerant bears first appeared on the river a week or more later than observed in previous years, and three regular adults from earlier years were not seen at all.

Their tendency to avoid people leaves the less tolerant adult bears fewer opportunities to fish at Brooks River than the habituated adults have. During July, an habituated adult would spend about a third more time, on average, fishing Brooks River than would a nonhabituated adult. During autumn, an habituated adult would spend twice as much time on the river as would a less tolerant adult. Again, learning to tolerate people gave habituated bears more access to fishing.

Subadult pauses to look for other bears while eating salmon, autumn 1992.

*Beauty and her spring cubs alert to possible danger in
autumn 1988.*

Bears Will Be Bears

Encounters between bears and people are not always to our liking. Bears can respond aggressively and their curiosity and hunger sometimes bring us into conflict. Nonhabituated adult bears probably see people as a threat. Consequently, they are more likely to respond aggressively in a surprise encounter, although their aggression will almost always be no more than a bluff charge. On the other hand, habituated adults seem to see people as innocuous animals in their environment, and subadults quickly learn that people are less a threat to them than are larger bears. Thus, habituated adults and subadults are more likely to damage property or get food from people.

Bluff Charges

If people surprise a bear in a close encounter, the bear may respond aggressively, especially a female with cubs. A mother lives constantly aware of the vulnerability of her cubs, and it takes her more time to lead cubs away from a threat than it takes for a single bear to flee. Consequently, a mother may sense no alternative but to respond aggressively to the sudden approach of a human.

Nonhabituated females are more likely to perceive people as a threat and respond aggressively. Nevertheless, habituated mothers will charge if they perceive a threat to their cubs and should be treated with great respect. Charges at Brooks River have resulted in only one minor injury in recent history.

Bluff charges vary in intensity from a short hop toward a person to a full run with ears back and head down. Some bears swat the air as they run and may also roar. Bears typically stop several feet short of the person and may huff before moving off. Often the bear has charged and gone before a person has time to react.

Curiosity and Habituation

Subadults and yearling cubs of habituated mothers are the bears most likely to be involved in the ursine equivalent of vandalism. Although these bears are probably avoiding larger bears by using areas near people, once there the irrepressible curiosity of subadults and yearlings can take control. Whenever young bears seek to learn about the strange human environment, humans perceive mischief and sometimes respond aggressively. Almost daily, park and lodge staff chase young bears out of the developed area surrounding Brooks Lodge. Sometimes they use firecracker shells and plastic bullets to teach the young bears that this human world is not a pleasant place to be.

Most property damage occurs during autumn, especially in years of strong salmon runs when the bears are catching fish easily and the tension among them seems reduced. The bears have more time to investigate people's things, especially after the lodge has closed and there are no people to chase them away. Just as the subadults become more playful, they also seem more curious. Yearling cubs also begin wandering farther from their mothers who seem to have little choice but to follow. In most years, anything that can be pulled, pawed, or chewed is somehow affected. Vulnerable equipment is often damaged, all removable covers are removed, and most things with strong odors are investigated.

The curiosity of Goatee's surviving cub Chowmane led the family into Brooks Lodge and campground many times. In 1990, Chowmane seemed fascinated with glass. She would paw plexiglass sign covers and stretch up to get her muzzle to windows.

Her mother did not wean her as a two-year-old in 1991, and the pair again frequented the lodge and campground when they were not fishing. During early July, they often walked through the campground when moving between the river and their bedding areas.

Their pattern abruptly changed after rangers finally caught young Chowmane in the campground and fired five firecracker shells behind her. She sprinted through the tall grass to catch her mother who was already fleeing the explosions. The pair seemed to learn that shouting campers might lead to something worse, and they stopped using that area. Fortunately, Chowmane never found human food during her time around buildings and tents.

Food-conditioning

The worst thing that people can teach bears is that people may mean a meal. Since the constant driving force in a bear's life is finding enough food to survive the winter and following spring, it will relentlessly explore all possible opportunities for a meal.

Bears learn quickly. Just once finding food that is associated with people, even by location or odor, is sometimes enough to cause a bear to seek it again in similar circumstances. Each success reinforces the association of people and food. Subadults and habituated adults are predisposed to learning this association, known as food-conditioning, because their frequent encounters with people make them likely to discover unsecured human food or garbage.

It is difficult to keep a bear from food. Few barriers can withstand a determined bear's strength, and food cannot be disguised or hidden from a bear's unmatched sense of smell. Brooks Lodge manager Perry Mollan once observed a bear detect less than a teaspoon of dried soup mix that was in a small slick float-

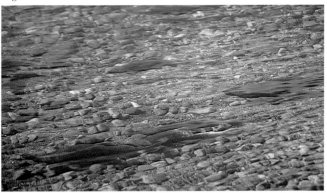

Sockeye salmon in spawning color at Brooks River during autumn.

Wary subadult eats spawned salmon in autumn 1992.

Two Nonhabituated Mothers

In 1988 and 1989, the nonhabituated female Lucy used Brooks River alone, quietly avoiding people. In July 1990, she returned to the river with one spring cub. She used the cutbank for a few days when no anglers were there, and she completely avoided Brooks Falls. She continued her shy ways in the autumn, avoiding both people and bears as she fished the cutbank.

In July 1991, Lucy returned with a large yearling cub. To feed him, she needed access to the rich fishing at Brooks Falls. Unexpectedly, she chose to rest and bed near the falls viewing platform despite the constant traffic of visitors. She probably chose the lesser threat of people over that of larger bears, most of whom stayed away from the viewing platform. Intolerant of people, as well as protective of her cub, she bluff-charged people several times that July.

When Lucy returned after Brooks Lodge had closed that September, her yearling cub had grown as large as some two-year-old subadults. Lucy continued to be extremely protective, but her yearling had other ideas. With no siblings, the yearling cub began looking for playmates. He would fish and play with groups of subadults, sometimes for more than an hour, wandering hundreds of yards from his mother.

Ester (left) plays with Lucy's yearling, autumn 1991.

The stress on Lucy was obvious. The yearling would seldom follow her. She sat, sometimes out of view in tall grass or brush, watching her yearling cub play with the subadults. She would yawn and salivate, sometimes vocalizing, all obvious signs of stress. On some occasions, she charged the subadult playmates and chased them away. Only then would the yearling cub follow her, as she huffed and popped her jaw to lead him away. Unsuspecting people sometimes walked into these situations, and Lucy charged. By the end of the year, fourteen bluff charges could be attributed to this one protective mother.

The female Flame was an interesting contrast to Lucy. Although intolerant of people like Lucy, Flame apparently found the task of protecting her cubs less stressful. She was a successful mother, probably weaning two two-year-olds in the spring of 1989. Flame was the largest female using Brooks River, where she fished only during autumn.

Alone in the autumn of 1989, Flame avoided people, using the cutbank when anglers were not there. Once when she caught scent of us in the observation stand, she sprinted from the river into the woods.

The next autumn she needed to feed her three spring cubs. She would tolerate anglers and continue fishing the cutbank as long as she could see them and they stayed far enough downriver. However, when people surprised her bedded cubs or approached too fast for her to lead them away, she responded with intimidating bluff charges, five that autumn.

In the autumn of 1991, Flame's three yearling cubs became curious about the world beyond mother. Although they did not play with subadults, they did lead mother to Brooks Lodge on several occasions. Flame became upset when they encountered people. She would pop her jaw as she tried to lead her family away, yet she did not charge that year.

ing into Naknek Lake. The bear ran from more than thirty yards on a direct line to the tiny slick and lapped it up.

Food-conditioned bears can become aggressive when seeking food from people. Such behavior sometimes leads to human injury, but more often to the death of the bear.

Serious bear incidents have been rare at Brooks River. There has not been a serious human injury caused by bears since 1966. There are no historical records of a human fatality caused by bears at Brooks River. The National Park Service has not had to destroy a bear since 1983, when it was judged that a food-conditioned female with two yearling cubs had become too aggressive with people.

This excellent record has resulted from two things. First, the National Park Service and Katmai National Park have progressive rules and regulations concerning the storage and handling of human food, garbage, and fish caught by anglers. The staff of the park and Brooks Lodge, as well as knowledgeable guides and concerned visitors, go to great lengths to insure that bears do not get food from people. Second, Katmai has been blessed with salmon runs numbering in the millions. The availability of these fish provides bears with a diet as rich as anything that they could obtain from people. Therefore, when mistakes do occur and bears get food from people in Katmai, those bears do not seem to seek more food from people as desperately as they might otherwise.

Unfortunately, the story does not end at the boundaries of Katmai National Park. Many young bears, especially males, eventually leave areas that they used with their mothers. Such dispersals can bring these bears to places where human food and garbage are managed less strictly. If these bears habituated to people in the park, then they are more likely to learn that the landfills, garbage dumpsters, fishing nets, camps, and cabins that they encounter mean food. When these bears aggressively seek food from people, they may be killed.

The number of subadult bears from Brooks River that have met such an end is unknown.

Goatee eats a salmon caught below Brooks Falls, July 1982.

Going Their Separate Ways

A pair of two-year-old siblings used the mouth of the river near Brooks Lodge regularly in autumn 1988. They encountered people and occasionally wandered among the buildings, causing rangers to chase them away. Their interactions with people, though, seemed innocuous.

The pair returned in July the next year, a little larger and more confident. They frequently grazed grasses and forbs growing near the lodge, apparently still not very successful at competing for good fishing. Their play became less amusing to people when the pair would sprint down the main path past the buildings. Although the male remained fairly docile toward people, the female began to test her relationship with them. When she approached, she seemed to expect people to get out of her way.

The female's approaches eventually resulted in her getting a fish from an angler. She was a fast learner and quickly perfected an approach to test anglers. She would lope toward them in a bounding gait with her head and ears up. Then she would stop short, expecting them to withdraw so that she could search for a fish. Anglers who understood bears would not reward her behavior, but those who had little experience with bears could become frightened and sometimes ran. Unfortunately, her behavior was reinforced by too many successes which encouraged her to approach anglers more often.

Her fish stealing ended with July as the bears left the river. She passed through Brooks River in September but was not identified there again. The male of the pair never learned that people could mean food and began to avoid people by the next year.

Although access to areas occupied by people may appear to be a competitive advantage for habituated mothers, it certainly is not in the long run if it leads to the food-conditioning and eventual killing of their offspring.

The first time a bear gets food from people usually results from a chance opportunity. Whether the bear later begins to seek food from people will somewhat be a consequence of its level of habituation to people as well as its need for food.

The only record of a nonhabituated adult getting human food was that of Beauty and her yearlings finding some abandoned packs in 1989. She did not later seek food from people. Habituated adults have many more opportunities to take food from people because of their frequent encounters with them. Old Mom found some lunches that had been carelessly left unattended for only a few minutes at the bridge in August 1991.

Still these competitive adults rarely seek out people as a source of food at Brooks River. Even though Diver regularly fished the oxbow and mouth near anglers, he never stole their fish. His own dominance and fishing skills provided for his needs. Bullet approached anglers many times as a subadult but rarely did so once he became competitive at Brooks Falls. Old Mom's pursuit of two men carrying a fish in 1989 occurred when her hungry yearling cubs were in the lead.

The problem of food-conditioning at Brooks River is worst among subadults during July because they have a great need for food but are unable to compete for the good fishing spots at Brooks Falls. They have frequent opportunities to learn from their encounters with people because they are forced into the usually marginal fishing areas of the lower river. Unfortunately, uninformed visitors sometimes behave in ways that contribute to excessively habituating and food-conditioning these young bears. Photographers who stay too close to bears give them opportunities to learn how people respond to them–a few subadults have learned how to herd people from such encounters. Anglers who continue fishing as bears approach give them opportunities to learn how to steal fish from people.

The rules of Katmai National Park require people to remain specified distances from bears. As long as people remain far away from bears, the bears will not excessively habituate, and are then much less likely to become food-conditioned. These distance rules thereby serve to protect both bears and people.

The Offspring of Habituated Mothers

Petite had long before learned to ignore anglers as she searched the lower river for scraps and injured salmon with her yearling cub in July 1988. She took no notice of anglers landing fish in the distance.

One day by the cutbank island, a lone angler failed to withdraw, apparently deciding that his fishing should not be interrupted by the approach of two small bears. He hooked a fish and played it into the shallow water by the gravel bar. Petite knew nothing about human fishing, but she did know that a fish splashing in shallow water meant vulnerable prey. In a moment, she had the fish off his line. She shared it with her yearling. Petite had never before responded to anglers landing fish; but afterwards her ears perked up and she looked whenever she heard the sound of a fish dragging line from a reel.

In 1990, Petite sometimes used the river mouth, and people crowded to watch and photograph her three new cubs. The once shy spring cubs had become comfortable with people by autumn. On October 15, a professional photographer left his tripod and walked to within ten yards of the intensely curious cubs to use a smaller lens. Having grown accustomed to the thoughtless approaches of this and some other photographers, Petite continued fishing undisturbed fifteen yards beyond the cubs.

One of Petite's offspring learned to fish from the bridge in 1992.

This pattern continued during 1991. Consequently, rangers had to drive the family away from the buildings five times with firecracker shells. By September, at least one of her yearling cubs began to test its limits with people. It sometimes led the family towards people expecting them to move, and it twice tried short bluff charges.

Petite successfully weaned all three two-year-olds in 1992. The three small subadults frequented the river mouth during July as they had done with their mother, regularly intruding near Brooks Lodge and encountering people on the trails. A small bear followed a visitor carrying a bag of garbage in the campground and took the bag. One subadult from Petite's litter took a fish that an angler abandoned as the small bear approached. That subadult was later identified trying to steal fish from other anglers. His fish-stealing approaches ended with the abundance of spawned salmon in the autumn, although he continued to act boldly around people.

Unfortunately, the story of Petite's offspring is not unusual among habituated families. Old Mom's yearling cubs spent much of their time around the lodge in 1989, sometimes getting their mother into trouble. Yearlings in the lead, the family followed two men carrying a fish for over 100 yards until the men felt compelled to throw the fish into the lake. Unfortunately, the family got the fish. In 1990, Old Mom weaned at least two of this litter. The female subadult eventually got a fish from anglers and learned to approach anglers to search for abandoned fish.

Our Choice

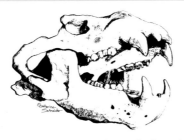

The interactions of bears and people at Brooks River are unique only in the large numbers of people involved. The process of how human use affects bears and their use of the river is the same at Brooks River as it is at many other salmon spawning streams where people visit to fish and view wildlife.

Throughout the Alaska Peninsula, Kodiak Island, and other coastal areas of Alaska and British Columbia, backcountry recreation in brown bear habitat is increasing in popularity. In Katmai National Park alone, sport fishing lodges regularly bring anglers to several backcountry streams in the interior and along the coast, large numbers of people float the Alagnak River, and bear viewing is attracting more people to backcountry areas as well as Brooks River.

We humans are inevitably a part of the bears' world: individual bears must either avoid us or learn to accept and perhaps exploit us. But a bear cannot think ahead to the ultimate consequences of its behavior around people. It only knows how to find food by responding to opportunities in its environment.

As human use of brown bear habitat increases, our impacts on bears are also growing. When people kill bears illegally or in self-defense, the events often receive media attention. However, the cumulative effects of our nonconsumptive use of bear habitat can be just as destructive to bear populations. Unlimited human use will eventually drive bears out, denying them access to productive habitat; the population will decrease as a result. Intermittent or limited human use may force bears to habituate or be locally denied access to salmon spawning streams and other habitat. If we behave irresponsibly around bears, they will learn behavior that can eventually lead to their destruction. We must be considerate in our use of bear habitat, and realize the consequences of our actions.

Subadult stands alert, autumn 1992.

Acknowledgments

Mark Wagner, Chief of Interpretation at Katmai National Park, encouraged us to write this book. Several people helped us collect data at Brooks River; we especially thank Scott Fitkin, Chris Garber, Brian Holmes, Wolfgang Maier, and Greg Wilker. Dr. Barrie Gilbert of Utah State University (USU) initiated this research project; he has dedicated much of his career to understanding the behavior and management of bears. The National Park Service funded the research from 1988 to 1991. Perry Mollan, manager of Brooks Lodge, gave us his perspective from more than a decade at Brooks River. Area biologists Victor Barnes, Donald Bill, Richard Russell, and Richard Sellers gave us helpful comments on the text.

The Authors

Tamara Olson received a master's degree from USU in 1993. In her study of bear and human of use of two salmon streams, she personally logged more than 2,400 observation hours. Ronald Squibb holds a doctorate in Range Science. He monitored bear-human interactions at Brooks River from 1989 to 1991, and logged more than 500 observation hours assisting Tamara. Photographer James Gavin worked seasonally as a maintenance worker at Katmai National Park and perfected his wildlife photography skills during off-duty time at Brooks River. Artist Catherine Schneider worked seasonally as a ranger and laborer for the park. Her love of the bears has found expression in her art.

The mouth of Brooks River and Naknek Lake, autumn 1992.